WORLD'S MOST
BAFFLING
PUZZLES

Charles Barry Townsend

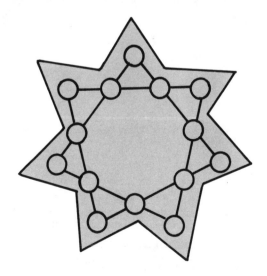

Sterling Publishing Co., Inc.   New York

Dedication

To Dwight Dobbins, the best cartoonist I've ever known.

Thanks, Dwight, for making the Puzzle Club come alive in our book and magazine collaborations. I look forward to other puzzling adventures on Old Oak Island in the future.

Edited by Jeanette Green

Library of Congress Cataloging-in-Publication Data

Townsend, Charles Barry.
    World's most baffling puzzles / Charles Barry Townsend.
       p. cm.
    Includes index.
    ISBN 0-8069-5832-4
    1. Puzzles. I. Title.
  GV1493.T684   1991
  793.73—dc20   91-21324
                                         CIP

10 9 8

First paperback edition published in 1992 by
Sterling Publishing Company, Inc.
387 Park Avenue South, New York, N.Y. 10016
© 1991 by Charles Barry Townsend
Distributed in Canada by Sterling Publishing
% Canadian Manda Group, P.O. Box 920, Station U
Toronto, Ontario, Canada M8Z 5P9
Distributed in Great Britain and Europe by Cassell PLC
Villiers House, 41/47 Strand, London WC2N 5JE, England
Distributed in Australia by Capricorn Link Ltd.
P.O. Box 665, Lane Cove, NSW 2066
Manufactured in the United States of America

Sterling ISBN 0-8069-5832-4 Trade
            0-8069-5833-2 Paper

Contents

Introduction

Once again I have the happy chore of welcoming our readers to another go at solving the world's most intriguing
puzzles. This is my fourth book for Sterling Publishing in
this series, and I'm happy to report that the material contained herein is every bit as interesting and challenging
as the problems presented in the preceding books. Once
again we've combed the archives of puzzledom to bring
you the widest possible variety of mental amusements.
Some of the conundrums awaiting you deal with juggling,
cards, and bottle caps. Tricky trials involving geography,
cocoa tins, an elevator, and a lighthouse are sure to test
your problem-solving abilities. As always, we've done our
best to find the most interesting and amusing illustra-
tions to accompany our presentation. So, sharpen your
pencils—and your wits—and get set to tackle over 90 of
the *World's Most Baffling Puzzles.*

Charles Barry Townsend

PUZZLES

The World's Most Baffling "Number" Puzzle

To solve the puzzle just arrange the four *fives* in the above winning picture so that their collective value equals 56.

The World's Most Baffling "Juggling" Puzzle

W. C. Fields, who began his career as a juggler, is shown here balancing a priceless crystal vase on top of a plate. Mr. Fields assures us that we can master this feat with only one minute of practice. See if you can figure out how before looking up the answer.

The World's Most Baffling "Business Card" Puzzle

Desperate Desmond, the local con artist, has a new scam. So, watch out! First he bends down the two opposite corners of his business card. He then places the card on the table so that it stands on these two corners. Desmond then bets everyone present that they can't blow the card over. When all have failed, he bets them that he can flip it over with a single puff. Can you figure out how this natty bag-of-wind accomplishes this bit of trickery?

The World's Most Baffling "Ornament" Puzzle

Old Saint Nick has a smashing Xmas puzzle for you. After fastening an ornament to one end of a three-foot piece of string, he tied the other end to an overhead bunch of mistletoe.

"I'll double your Xmas present," he said, "if you can cut that string right in the middle and not have the ornament fall and smash on the floor. Remember: Once you've cut through the string you can't touch the string or the ornament in any way."

What's it going to be, reader, two Mercedeses for Xmas or the old bituminous coal?

The World's Most Baffling "Card" Puzzle

You don't have to be a magician to solve this problem, but your friends will think you are. Tell them you're going to show them a puzzle based on lightning calculation. After discarding all the face cards and tens from the pack, take the remaining cards, and start laying them down on the table in groups of three. Explain to your audience that each group of three cards forms a three-digit number that can be divided by 11 without leaving a remainder. You form these three-digit numbers as fast as you can lay down the cards.

In our example we have the number 231. Eleven goes into this number exactly 21 times. How is this marvelous feat accomplished?

The World's Most Baffling "Bottle Cap" Puzzle

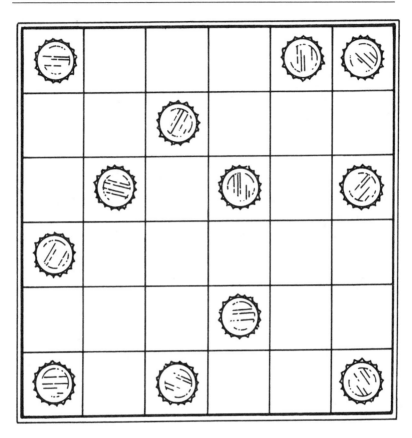

This is a real stopper of a puzzle besides being a darn good solitaire game. First, lay out a game board with six squares to a side as pictured above. Then round up 12 bottle caps and you're ready to play. The object of the puzzle is to place the bottle caps in 12 different squares on the board in such a manner that no more than 2 caps are in the same row—horizontally, vertically, or diagonally.

We provide one answer at the back of the book, but I think there are many more.

The World's Most Baffling "Cross" Puzzle

The Reverend I. N. Spire is once again in a spiritual quandary. Last night, during a tremendous rainstorm, a gust of wind toppled the cross from the church steeple, sending it spinning to the ground where it split into five pieces. Sexton Winslow has vowed to mend the cross and return it to its perch of distinction, if he can only figure out how to reassemble the pieces. A revelation is definitely in order. Can you help the Reverend and Winslow see the light and solve this mystery?

The World's Most Baffling "Business Survey" Puzzle

From the looks of things, I'd say Sylvester's Surveys is a booming concern. Just don't ask them about the mustard account that got away. They were hired by the Volcano Mustard Company to find out how many people like hot mustard and how many like mild. The report they presented reads:

Number of people surveyed..................300
Number of hot mustard users 234
Number of mild mustard users 213
Number who used both hot and mild..........144
Number who never used mustard 0

After the Volcano Mustard Company digested this report, they erupted and promptly fired Sylvester's Surveys for gross inaccuracies. Can you spot the errors in their report?

The World's Most Baffling "Water and Wine" Puzzle

Mr. Percy Poindexter, the famous after-dinner puzzle expert, is shown here at his wit's end trying to solve the old Water and Wine puzzle. It goes like this: You have two glasses each filled with exactly the same amount of liquid. One contains water, the other, wine. First take a teaspoon of water from the water glass and pour it into the wine glass. Next stir the wine and water until well mixed. Then take a teaspoon of the water and wine mixture and pour it into the glass of water.

The question now is: is there more wine in the water glass than water in the wine glass, or is there less?

The World's Most Baffling "Elevator" Puzzle

This picture of a rather ornate 1870s Otis Elevator brings to mind a story we heard recently. It seems that every morning, at 8 AM, a businessman would leave his apartment on the 45th floor and ride the self-service elevator to the lobby level where his limo was outside waiting for him. Every evening he returned to the building and rode the same elevator up to the 40th floor, where he got out and walked up the remaining five floors to his apartment. Once in a while he rode all the way to the 45th floor, but this only happened occasionally. Can you explain the rather eccentric behavior of this gentleman?

The World's Most Baffling "Cardboard" Puzzle

"All right, ladies and gentlemen, the next item on our program is the Cross-to-Square contest. The contestants must cut the cardboard cross into four equal pieces that can then be put together to form a perfect square. The hitch is that the square must be the same height and width as the cross before it was cut up. On your mark, get set, start snipping."

The World's Most Baffling "Planchette" Puzzle

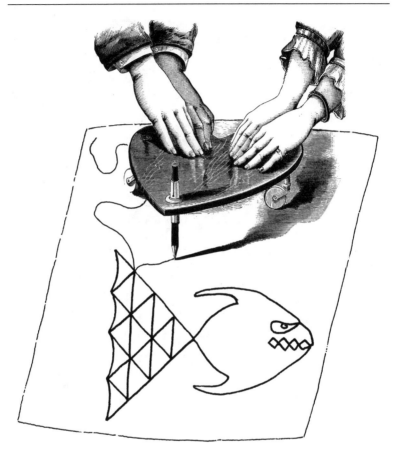

You don't have to be clairvoyant to solve this puzzle, but it sure would help! Paul and Vivian are shown here communicating with what looks like the spirit of a Siamese Fighting Fish. I don't know how they did it, but I'm told that the planchette drew this picture with a single line and that the pencil never left the paper nor did the line ever cross itself at any point. Do you think that you can duplicate this drawing while adhering to these other-worldly rules?

The World's Most Baffling "India Squares" Puzzle

This Indian prince of puzzlers is on his way to a puzzle convention in Agra. Printed on the cloth that covers the royal elephant is his contribution to the lively arts. To solve it, you must determine how many squares, both big and small, are contained within the drawing. You have five minutes before the caravan moves on.

The World's Most Baffling "Diner" Puzzle

In our illustration Hash House Harriet is calling out for an order of eggs on toast. We've arranged the sentence to form a tasty puzzle for you to solve. If you replace each letter with a number, using the same number for the same letter wherever it appears, you can make a correct mathematical expression out of her colorful mode of speech. Since there are several answers to this puzzle, you must come up with the answer that will give you the highest possible total.

The World's Most Baffling "Geography" Puzzle

Our next problem is a lesson in geography. Hidden in the above chart are the names of four cities, all beginning with the same letter. To find them, you must first find the letter in question and then proceed to spell out the names going in four different directions. With the exception of the first letter, no letter in the chart is used twice.

The World's Most Baffling "Cocoa Tin" Puzzle

In this sweet problem you are given a sealed tin of Baker's Breakfast Cocoa, full of cocoa, and a twelve-inch ruler. Can you measure the inside of the tin, without opening it, to determine the length of the box's major diagonal line?

An example would be a line from the right bottom front corner (B) of the can to the left top back corner (A). There are four of these lines inside the tin. Disregard the thickness of the tin's sides, top, and bottom. Your final measure may be within a quarter inch of the actual length. You could solve the problem by resorting to mathematical calculations, but there's an easier method that relies on straight measuring with the ruler only. We want this method.

We've excluded dimensions from the problem, since the solution is not dependent upon them. Do you think that you can brew up a quick solution to this rich puzzle?

The World's Most Baffling "Racing" Puzzle

Pictured above are the three prize winners in the Ladies International Cup held in Brooklyn, New York in the summer of 1897. It began as a nine-horse race, but the number 1 horse threw a shoe and never finished. The remaining horses were numbered 2 through 9. An interesting fact concerning the race is that if you add together the numbers of the three winning steeds, the sum would be the same as the total of the numbers on the five losing mounts.

Of the three winners, the one with the lowest number finished first, the highest number finished third, and the second-place winner's number was one greater than the number of the winning horse. Can you figure out the numbers of the three victorious thoroughbreds?

The World's Most Baffling "Counter" Puzzle

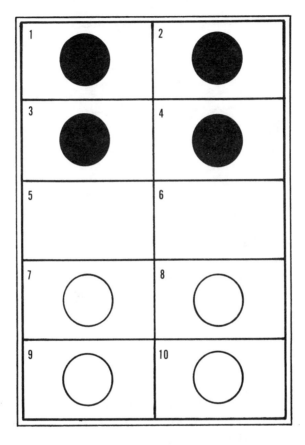

For this problem you'll need four black and four white counters placed on your puzzle board as shown above. What you're challenged to do is to make these eight pieces change place in exactly ten moves.

The rules of play are simple. Black moves down the board and white moves up. All pieces must either move forward to an empty square or jump over one or two counters to get to an empty square. You have ten minutes to solve this one.

The World's Most Baffling "Lighthouse" Puzzle

The following tale concerns the harrowing experience of Lonesome Leroy, a lighthouse keeper. It seems that one night, while taking a bath, the water faucets broke and Leroy couldn't turn them off. When the water started spilling over the rim of the tub, Leroy tried to leave the bathroom, but he found that the door was stuck and wouldn't open. As the water flooded the room and rose up to his chin, Leroy looked for a way to escape. The room was solid stone and had no windows or other means of escape. It was at this moment that Leroy thought of a solution that would save him from drowning. Do you know what he did?

The World's Most Baffling "Bathtub" Puzzle

Professor Willard Wordsworth, a resident of Ma Bascomb's boardinghouse, has made these observations about the gas-fired Victorian tub in the second-floor bathroom: You can fill the tub from the cold water tap in 6 minutes and 40 seconds, while it takes exactly 8 minutes to fill it from the hot water tap. Furthermore, after the tub is full, if you pull out the stopper, it takes the water exactly 13 minutes and 20 seconds to run out.

Now comes Willard's puzzle. If you leave the stopper out and open both the hot and cold water taps all the way, how long will it take to fill the tub? Don't get all wet trying to solve this one.

The World's Most Baffling "Antique" Puzzle

Calvin Collectable has selected the above twelve items from his antique shop for you to use in our next puzzle. Calvin challenges you to arrange these items into six rows with each row containing four items. Some items can, of course, appear in more than one row.

The World's Most Baffling "Touching" Puzzle

You may think that you'll have to resort to some magical solution to solve this problem after you've worked at it for awhile. Place the five magician's palming coins here so that each coin will be touching every other coin. If you're out of palming coins, you may use quarters or half-dollars. Our Baffling Bunny thinks that ten minutes is tops for finding the answer to this problem.

The World's Most Baffling "Telephone Pole" Puzzle

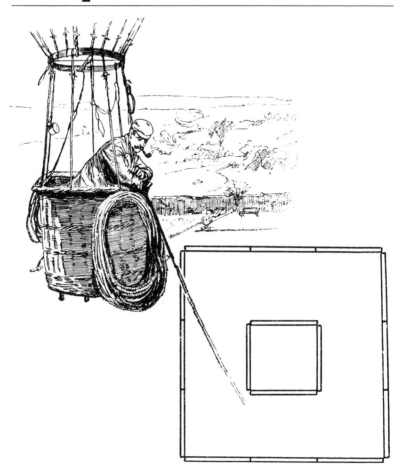

Squire Bishop, an avid puzzler from way back, has been challenged by the local telephone company to a battle of wits. The linemen laid out 16 telephone poles on the grounds of his estate in the form of one small square in the middle of a larger square. The problem is to move four of the poles to new positions so that three squares will be formed. The squire is obviously up in the air over this one.

The World's Most Baffling "Milling" Puzzle

"What do you say, Ian, will you mill my corn for one-twentieth of the amount of corn I bring you?"

"Are you daft, Angus? You know full well that my price is one-tenth of the corn brought to my mill!"

Oh well, you can't blame Angus for trying. However, he's faced with a problem. How much corn must he bring to the mill so that after giving Ian his ten percent he will come away with exactly 100 pounds of cornmeal?

Assume there will be no waste during the milling.

The World's Most Baffling "Golf Tees" Puzzle

Andrew MacDivot's form on the tee certainly leaves much to be desired. However, when it comes to winning a drink at the 19th hole, Andrew has a bagful of great golf puzzles. In the one pictured here the puzzler must move 2 of the golf tees to new positions so that there are 4 equilateral triangles instead of 3. Try solving this one before tee time.

The World's Most Baffling "Soda Straws" Puzzle

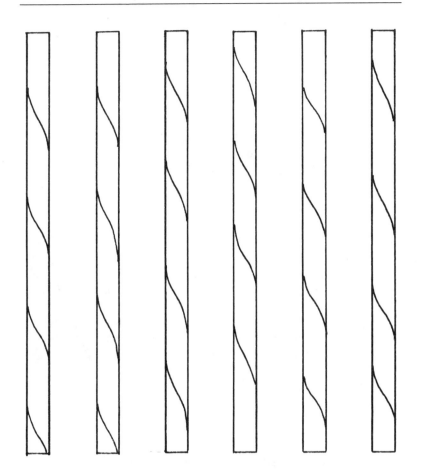

The next time you go down to the local malt shop, try stumping friends with this one. As shown here, lay out six soda straws on the table and say: "Using these straws, I can prove to you that six plus five equals nine. By adding five more straws to the ones on the table, I'll end up with nine instead of eleven."

Can you figure out how to do this ex-straw-dinary puzzle?

The World's Most Baffling "Math" Puzzle

1 2 3 4 5 6 7 8 9 = 100

ADD TWO MINUS SIGNS (−)

ADD ONE PLUS SIGN   (+)

That nonpareil of substitute teachers, Ms. Priscilla Sunshine, is back to test your mathematical prowess.

"All right students, pay attention! The problem on the board is patently incorrect. However, if you were to place two minus signs (−) and one plus sign (+) between certain of the numbers on the left side of the equation, you would end up with a correct mathematical expression that equals 100. You have until the end of the period to discover where to place these signs."

The World's Most Baffling "Magic Square" Puzzle

Our famous Puzzle Computer seems to have contracted some sort of hacker virus. The program was supposed to have generated a magic square that would add up to six in every horizontal, vertical, and diagonal direction. Instead, it came up with the above dismal display. Can you rearrange the numbers on the screen so that the correct magic square is formed?

The World's Most Baffling "Line" Puzzle

Once again those two famous archaeologists, Hawkings and Petrie, have uncovered a puzzle treasure from the past. Let's listen in:

"Petrie, this could well be the oldest recorded puzzle in history. We'll be famous!"

"For once, Hawkings, you may be right! According to the hieroglyphics, you must draw the pyramid pictured here using one continuous line. At no point can the line cross itself or go back over any part already drawn. If we dig deeper we may come across the answer!"

Let's see if our readers can dig up the answer before sundown.

The World's Most Baffling "Sculpture" Puzzle

"I say, Millicent, that's a smashing new puzzle sculpture you've put in your garden. What's the problem behind it?"

"It's an original Oliver Weldright creation, Percy. To solve the puzzle you must figure out where Oliver could weld three straight bars across it so that the bars would cut once through each of the squares that make up the sculpture. I'll give you until teatime to come up with the answer!"

The World's Most Baffling "Ice Cream Stick" Puzzle

Here's a puzzle that's a real stickler! Mrs. Murbles, that purveyor of all things cold and tasty, has come up with another of her delightful puzzles. Above she has laid out a Roman numeral equation using ice cream sticks. It's not right, but you can correct it without touching any of the sticks. That sounds impossible but I assure you it can be done. Don't melt before the challenge.

The World's Most Baffling "Ports of Call" Puzzle

(1) GLSOLESANE   (6) LMRSLAEEIS
(2) NONODL   (7) BGNOYMEATO
(3) IEDERIJOONAR   (8) DVNOMIOETE
(4) SNILOB   (9) SREBT
(5) LHANCTORSE   (10) NDNGELRIA

The old salt pictured here has had many a landfall in his fifty years at sea. In his snug harbor at Shelter Cove he challenges you to unscramble the names of ten world seaports that he has visited. You have until four bells to come up with the answers.

The World's Most Baffling "Shooting" Puzzle

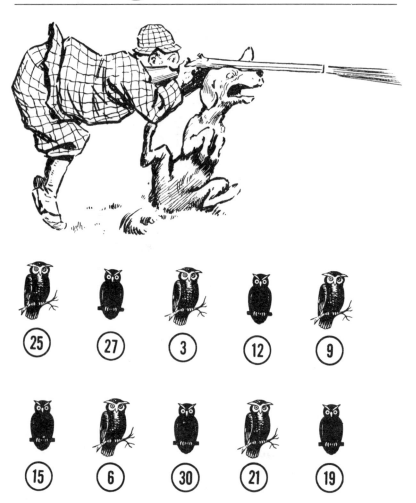

At a recent charity fete Barney Blunderbuss, the local skeet champion, was trying to win a prize at the shooting gallery concession. You get three shots for ten dollars, and if you knock down three birds whose numbers add up to exactly 50, you win a stuffed alligator. Care to take a turn after Barney runs out of money?

The World's Most Baffling "Thimble" Puzzle

Thomas Thackery, the king of Thaumaturgical Thimble Trickery, has just won a month's free dry cleaning from the proprietor of the Lost Button Laundry Service by stumping him with this puzzle. Thomas bet him that he couldn't arrange three stick matches so that they could support a thimble. The hard part was that: (A) the thimble must touch all three matches; (B) the thimble could not touch any part of the table; (C) the thimble could not touch a match head; and (D) none of the match heads could touch the table. Also, the matches could not be bent or broken, and none of these items could hang over the edge of the table. Can you duplicate Thomas's feat?

The World's Most Baffling "Zoo" Puzzle

Walter Snaretrap, park commissioner at the local zoo, had a problem trying to confine a group of animals. It seems that the lion no longer wished to lie down with the lamb, so to speak. Snaretrap had placed nine assorted animals in one square enclosure. After a while the lions started nipping at the camels, and the elephants stomped on the lions. So, no one was very happy. Snaretrap decided it was time for each of the animals to have a pen of its own. To do this, he built two more square enclosures inside the first enclosure. This created nine separate pens. Do you know where he placed these enclosures?

The World's Most Baffling "Mind-Over-Matter" Puzzle

That world famous mentalist, the Great Zamboni, challenges the reader to a test of wills. First, stand a nickel on edge, and then gently balance a paper match across the top. Next, cover both the coin and the match with an inverted glass. Now for the experiment. You must cause the match to move or fall off the coin without touching the table or the glass or causing them to move in any way. You are not allowed to stamp your feet or to make any kind of loud noise. The Great Zamboni claims that he can make the match move using only his brain waves, but there is another way. How do you think the feat can be accomplished?

The World's Most Baffling "Clock" Puzzle

It never rains but it pours for the good Reverend I. N. Spire. Not only did he lose the steeple cross during that monumental rainstorm (see page 12), but the clockface was also broken into four pieces by a flying branch. When he examined the damage, he noted an extraordinary thing. The Roman numerals on each piece independently added up to twenty. Can you figure out how the clockface split to make this occur?

The World's Most Baffling "Poem" Puzzle

Here we see Mr. and Ms. Gotrocks leading their dinner party to the table. Mr. Gotrocks has been entertaining his guests with a series of puzzles and stumpers. I think that his wife has had quite enough of his posturing, as evidenced by the puzzle she's giving him as they enter the dining room. Can you decipher the cryptic four-line rhyme contained in the above poser?

The World's Most Baffling "Baseball" Puzzle

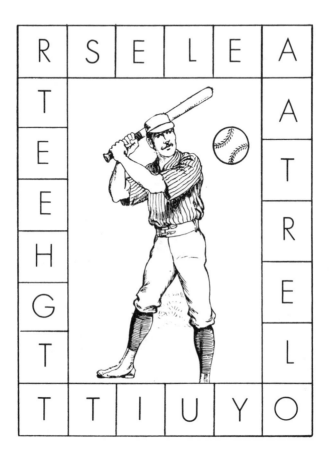

Here's a grand slam puzzle for all of you baseball fans. Over the past 100 years, much has been said about our national pastime. We've picked out one of the most famous quotations concerning the philosophy of the game and arranged the letters round the ballplayer above. Let's see if you can find the quotation. Starting at any letter, go around the frame twice reading every other letter as you go.

The World's Most Baffling "Word" Puzzle

$$99 + 9 = 9$$

At the turn of the century, Professor Otto Doppelganger was one of Europe's leading puzzle experts. Here we see him dictating his memoirs into an early Edison recording machine. Let's listen in:

"And then, in the summer of 1899, I invented my most famous puzzle, the Nifty Nines Impossibility. I proved that ninety-nine plus nine is equal to nine if you add a certain five-letter word to the equation. That word was . . ."

We've left out the professor's answer. Can you figure out what that nifty five-letter word was?

The World's Most Baffling "Big Fish" Puzzle

The fisherman pictured here certainly had a whale of a story to tell his friends when he got back to shore. It seems his prayers were answered; the leviathan passed him by. How big was this fish? Well, the fisherman's best guess is that the fish's head was 60 feet long, the fish's tail was as long as its head and half of its body, and the fish's body was half of its entire length. How long do you calculate this denizen of the deep was?

The World's Most Baffling "State" Puzzle

"We've been aloft for two days now. What state do you think we're flying over?"

"That's an easy question, Wilbur. It's the only state whose name begins with, ends with, and has every other letter the same. I'll give you until we land in ten minutes to solve that one!"

The World's Most Baffling "Dice" Puzzle

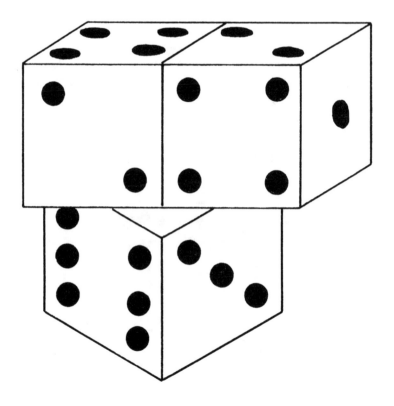

You'll need three dice for this problem. Place one die on the table, and hold the other two between thumb and forefinger. Wager those present that they cannot place these two dice side-by-side on top of the die on the table at an angle as depicted in the above picture. Needless to say, they will fail every time. When they finally concede defeat, pick up the dice and balance them without hesitation. The only question is . . . how are you going to do it?

The World's Most Baffling "Checker" Puzzle

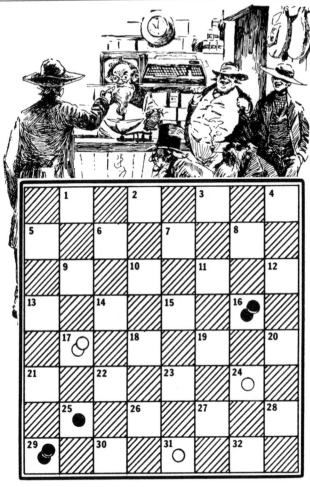

Pop Bentley is at it again. He's won 78 straight games of checkers down at the general store. Above is the end of his last game with Cy Corncrib this morning. Pop was playing the white pieces and it was his turn. The white pieces are moving up the board, while the black are moving down. Can you figure out what moves Pop used to beat his arch rival?

The World's Most Baffling "Shopping" Puzzle

Tilly the Tireless was certainly born to shop. When the notice about a mallwide sale appeared, she beat it down to the Bon Ton department store for some serious outfitting. At the checkout counter of one store, her total bill, including tax, came to $103. Tilly rummaged through her purse and came up with eight bills that totaled exactly $103. The funny thing was that none of them were one-dollar bills. Can you figure out what combination of greenbacks Tilly used to pay her bill with?

The World's Most Baffling "Proofreading" Puzzle

"Frankly, Professor, I can't solve this problem. I was up all last night trying to find the blasted third incorrect item!"

"Same here, Professor. I've studied the paragraph for two days without finding it!"

Their are three errers in this paragraph. Study it carefully and see if you can find all of them.

The World's Most Baffling "Handshake" Puzzle

Once again it's graduation at the Apex Santa Claus School. This year eight new Kriss Kringles are ready to assume their duties at department stores across the city. As they get ready to leave, each santa shakes hands with each of the other santas. This brings us to our puzzle. How many handshakes will there be?

The World's Most Baffling "Maze" Puzzle

THE HAMPTON COURT MAZE

"When I was in England, I found my way to the center of the famous Hampton Court Maze and back out again while blindfolded. Since no one accompanied me in or out, can you figure out how I accomplished this impossible feat?"

Don't get lost trying this old chestnut by Claude "Bring 'Em Back Solved" Burroughs.

The World's Most Baffling "Logic" Puzzle

You'll need all of the pyramid power you can generate to solve this neat little logic problem. The numbers in the above triangle follow a certain pattern. If you can discern what this pattern is, you will then be able to calculate what numbers should replace the five question marks within the triangle. You have until the desert sands in this hourglass run out to find the answer.

The World's Most Baffling "Sticky Taffy" Puzzle

Here's a great Valentine's Day puzzle for your sweetheart. Along with the regular box of bonbons, give her twelve pieces of saltwater taffy arranged in the above invalid equation. Tell her that if she can move one of the pieces to a new position that will turn it into a correct equation, you will take her dining and dancing. On second thought, if she fails, take her anyway if you don't want another St. Valentine's Day Massacre.

The World's Most Baffling "Nail" Puzzle

Hiram Ballpeene, our local handyman, has a knack for creating construction puzzles. Above, he has laid out twelve nails so that they form three squares. The problem is to move three of these nails to new positions so that you'll have four squares. Let's see if you can hammer out the answer in less than five minutes.

The World's Most Baffling "Crown" Puzzle

Here we find a tower guard hard at work protecting the crown jewels of England. This stout lad spends many an hour gazing upon the greatest collection of riches in the world. While staring at a case containing 12 mounted crowns, Harold was suddenly struck with a puzzle inspiration. Would it be possible to connect these 12 crowns using 5 straight lines? Each line, of course, would have to start at the end of the previous line. After ten minutes of thought, Harold came up with the answer. Solve this one and we'll crown you Prince of Puzzlers!

The World's Most Baffling "Waiter" Puzzle

Clumsy Callahan was the fastest and the sloppiest waiter down at the Bavarian Gardens Restaurant. He drenched more diners than Hurricane Hugo. Finally, one day a disgusted customer left Callahan a one-cent tip and the following note: "You ruined my suit, so I'm leaving you a penny tip. However, if you can remove the penny from the plate without touching the table, the plate, or the penny, I'll give you a twenty-five dollar gratuity." Clumsy never solved this problem. Can you?

The World's Most Baffling "Mental" Puzzle

"Yes, I'm getting it now! The complete number is 198. Is that correct?"

Once again the Mental Wizard has read your mind. Here's how the feat is done. Ask someone to write down any three-digit number in which each digit is a different number. Next, tell him to reverse the number and then to subtract the smaller number from the larger number. Finally, ask him to tell you what the last digit of the difference is. In the above example that would be eight. With this information you can tell him what the complete number is. See if you can figure out the Wizard's modus operandi before looking in the answer section.

The World's Most Baffling "Presidential" Puzzle

Here's a presidential problem for you. According to the Constitution of the United States, a person must meet four requirements before becoming the leader of our great country. They are:

(1) The candidate must be 35 years of age or older.
(2) The candidate must have been born in the United States.
(3) The candidate must have lived here for at least 14 years.
(4) The candidate must _____ ?

We have given you the first three. Can you tell us what the fourth requirement is?

The World's Most Baffling "Rebus" Puzzles

Complete each rebus using associated clues.

The World's Most Baffling "H_2O" Puzzle

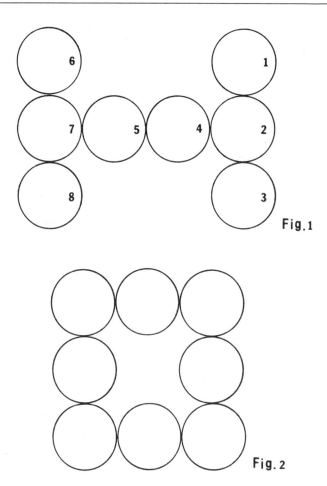

Fig. 1

Fig. 2

This is one of those delightful shifting coin problems. You have to change the H in Fig. 1 into the O in Fig. 2 in just five moves. A move consists of sliding one coin at a time to a new position without disturbing any of the other coins. When the coin reaches its new position, it must be touching two other coins. Don't end up all wet at the end of this slippery puzzle.

The World's Most Baffling "Rearranging" Puzzle

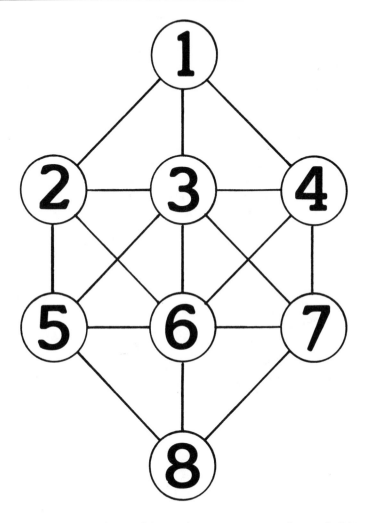

Here's a nice little problem to tax your puzzling abilities. The above connected circles contain the numbers 1 through 8. Your problem is to rearrange these numbers in the circles so that no two consecutive numbers will be joined by any one of the lines.

The World's Most Baffling "Addition" Puzzle

Professor Flunkum has just had the tables turned on him. In a weak moment he challenged his students to come up with a math problem that he couldn't solve. What they presented him was a problem in addition. To solve it, he has to arrange eight 8's so that when they are added up will they will total 1,000. Can you help the perplexed professor out?

The World's Most Baffling "Real Estate" Puzzle

Sidney, a local builder, divided up a 32-acre plot of land into eight building lots and put up a house on each one. Every lot in his development was exactly the same size and shape. Sidney's problem is that someone stole all the boundary markers from the lots and his estate plans are missing. He suspects foul play. Can you help Sidney determine where the original boundaries of each lot were? (The *H*'s indicate where each house was built.)

The World's Most Baffling "Campaign Button" Puzzle

That peerless vote-getter, Herman Gladhander, is nervously waiting for election results to be posted. To wile away the time, he's trying to solve a puzzle his campaign manager told him about. The object is to place 14 buttons on the table so that you have seven rows with four buttons in each row. Each button can, of course, be in more than one row. See if you can help Herman win at least one contest tonight.

The World's Most Baffling "Weighing" Puzzle

Pictured here is High Hat Louie, a famous old tea merchant in New York's Chinatown. He's standing here trying to figure out how to divide 20 pounds of tea into 10 2-pound packets using a simple balance scale. He could only find two weights around his shop; one was 5 pounds and the other was 9 pounds. He knows that it can be done in just nine weighings, but he's forgotten how to do it. Can you help High Hat solve this mystery before his customers start coming in?

The World's Most Baffling "Mystical Square" Puzzle

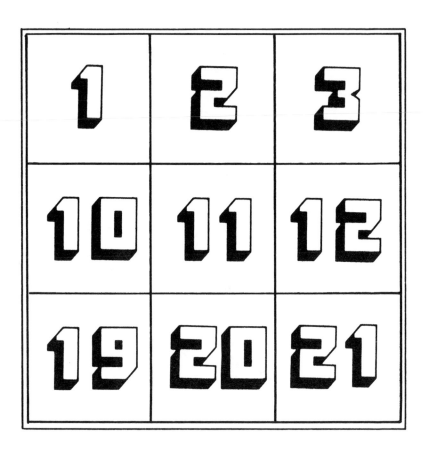

Let's take time out for another of those delightful (?) mystical square puzzles. All you have to do is rearrange the nine numbers in the above square so that every horizontal, vertical, and diagonal line adds up to 33. I hope that you can conjure up the answer in five minutes or less.

The World's Most Baffling "Substitution" Puzzle

It looks like everyone has the answer to the extra credit problem in Ms. Sunshine's math class. In case you're not familiar with this type of puzzle, you must substitute the numbers 0 through 9 for the ten different letters in the above math expression. The finished product must be a correct addition problem. The same number is given to each occurrence of the same letter.

The World's Most Baffling "Progression" Puzzle

Here we have an old-time kid trying to solve an old-time puzzle. Some things just never change!

The World's Most Baffling "Pencil" Puzzle

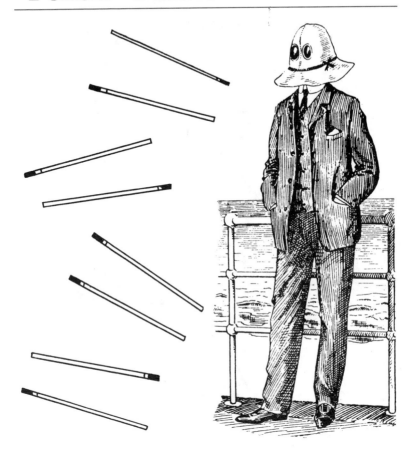

The mysterious passenger on A Deck has everyone on the S.S. Extravagantic buzzing with wonder. It's rumored that he won free passage on this around-the-world cruise by beating the captain with a simple puzzle. It seems that he bet the captain that he couldn't arrange eight pencils on the table so that they would form two squares and four triangles. Of course, you weren't allowed to break the pencils. See if you could have won a free ride on this princely bucket.

The World's Most Baffling "Train" Puzzle

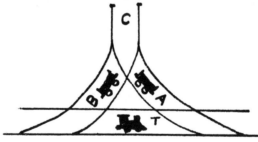

When Peter Cooper built his famous locomotive, the Tom Thumb, there were only about 13 miles of railroad track in the United States. Near Baltimore there was a funny little siding that caused all kinds of mix-ups. In the diagram below, *T* is the engine and *A* and *B* are two cars on the siding. Position *C* is only long enough to hold one car or the engine. Your problem is to make cars *A* and *B* change places and to end up with the engine back where it started in the fewest possible moves.

The World's Most Baffling "Stirring" Puzzle

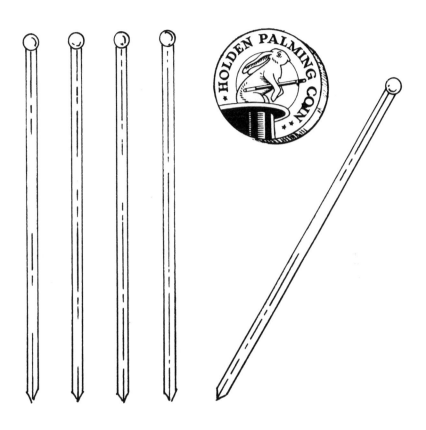

Here's a neat bet you can use the next time you're at the local soda fountain. Place four plastic stirrers and a coin on the table. Wager those present that they cannot pick up the four stirrers and the coin all at once using only a fifth stirrer. The catch is that after lifting them clear of the table the person must be able to turn the lifting stirrer over and still not have the other stirrers, or the coin, fall off. Levitate on that one for a while.

The World's Most Baffling "Map" Puzzle

"All right, Farquar, let's see how good your map skills really are. Tell me what the following American cities and towns have in common: Albany, Bridgeport, Jamestown, Lancaster, Lincoln, Menlo Park, Montclair, Newark, Richmond, Saratoga, and Wilmington."

"An interesting problem, Liverston. Does it have anything to do with latitude or longitude?"

The World's Most Baffling "O. Henry" Puzzle

"Oh dear, what shall I do? I only have $1.87 for Christmas presents!"

The opening of O. Henry's famous Christmas story, "The Gift of the Magi," reads:

"One dollar and eighty-seven cents. That was all. And sixty cents of it was in pennies . . . Three times Della counted it. One dollar and eighty-seven cents. And the next day would be Christmas."

His calculations about the money are wrong! Can you find his error?

The World's Most Baffling "Time" Puzzle

The gentleman pictured here is having nightmares over a puzzle he heard at work and has been unable to solve all day. The problem states that a woman had two clocks in her house. One of the clocks didn't run at all, and the other clock always loses an hour a day. Now, which of the clocks will have the correct time most often during any given week? Please solve this one in a hurry so this distraught man can get some sleep before dawn's early light.

The World's Most Baffling "Pie" Puzzle

There's nothing like a good pie puzzle when Turkey Day rolls around. This problem is so old that Governor Bradford probably used it at dessert during that first Thanksgiving Day so many years ago. What you have to determine is: What are the most different-size pieces you can cut this mincemeat pie into, by making four straight cuts across it?

The World's Most Baffling "Domino" Puzzle

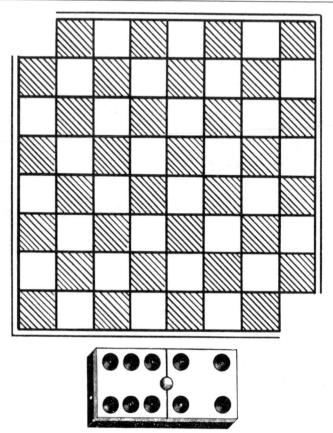

Here's your chance to play both checkers and dominoes at the same time. Let's say we have 32 dominoes and that each domino is big enough to cover two squares on a checkerboard. We could then place all of them on the board, and they would cover all 64 squares. Fair enough?

Now, let us cut off two opposite corner squares from the board and discard one of the dominoes. Could you then cover the remaining 62 squares on the board with the 31 dominoes you have left on the table? If you can, prove it. If you cannot, explain why.

The World's Most Baffling "Alphabet" Puzzle

```
A       F  HIJKLMNO QRS UWXY
BCDE G              P     T V
```

"And now, Mr. Applebee,
for the grand prize of . . .
ten dollars, where should
we place the final letter of
the alphabet, Z, above or
below the line? You have
30 seconds to answer the
question. Good luck!"

The World's Most Baffling "Chocolate Candy" Puzzle

Many years ago three travelers shared a table at the Black Eye Tavern. At the end of dinner they ordered a plate of chocolates to be shared equally. Before the candy arrived at the table, they had all fallen asleep. The first one to wake up saw the candy, ate his equal share, and fell back to sleep. The second man soon awoke and, seeing the chocolates, ate what he thought was his equal share and promptly went back to sleep. Finally, the third traveller awoke, looked at the candy, and ate what he thought was his equal share. He then drifted back to the Land of Nod.

While they snored away the rest of the evening, their waiter removed the dish with the candy on it. There were eight pieces left. Can you figure out how many pieces were originally brought to the table?

The World's Most Baffling "Tire" Puzzle

Not long ago our puzzle club set out for a day's outing at the local beach. Halfway there we had a flat tire. Our driver jacked the bus up, removed the bad tire, and went to get his spare. As he was about to put the spare on the wheel, he kicked the hubcap on the ground so hard that it flew off the side of the road and over a cliff, taking along the five lug nuts used to hold the tire on the wheel.

"Well, that does it," he said, "I'll have to walk back to the last town we passed and try to find some replacement lug nuts."

"Not so fast, sonny," Aunt Bertha piped up, "all you have to do is . . . !"

What was Aunt Bertha's solution to this motoring mishap?

The World's Most Baffling "Fencing" Puzzle

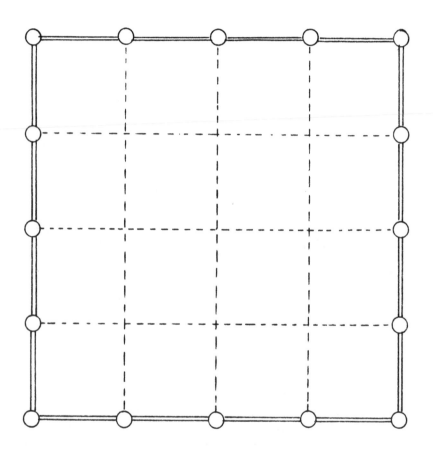

Farmer Brown had a plot of land that measured four acres by four acres. He had it fenced in with sixteen sections of fence. He proposed to divide this plot into four smaller plots. Each plot was to contain four square acres of farmland. He did this by adding an *odd number* of fence sections within the existing fencing. Can you determine where he placed them?

The World's Most Baffling "Shape" Puzzle

Back in 1877 Professor Reynaund put on quite a show. One of his most popular features was a puzzle slide show presented with the aid of his famous invention, the Praxinoscope. Here we see him presenting the problem known as "The Puzzling Shape." Shown on the screen, top to bottom, are the front and side views of a solid block of wood. After studying these two pictures, you should be able to figure out what the three-dimensional shape of the object is. Focus in on this one.

The World's Most Baffling "Family" Puzzle

"All the Anderson children, get down here on the double. Hup, hup, hup!"

Well, it looks like the Andersons really mean business this time. They've hired Cedric Longnose, the toughest baby-sitter in town, to watch their brood tonight. The Andersons have a great bunch of kids, but are they hard to handle. I forget just how many kids they have, but I do know that each daughter has the same number of brothers as she has sisters. Also, each of the boys has twice as many sisters as he has brothers. Using this information, can you figure out how many Anderson children there are?

The World's Most Baffling "Match" Puzzle

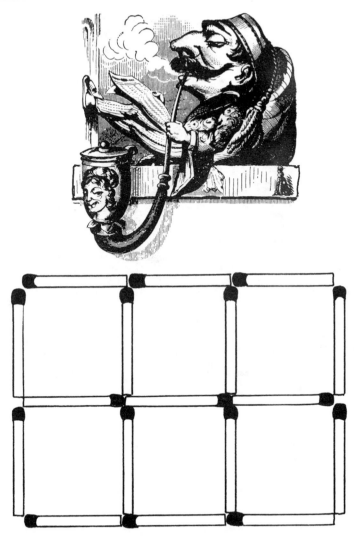

Mr. Puff has another of his inimitable match problems. He has laid out seventeen matches so that they form six equal squares. He invites you to remove five of them, so that you are left with only three squares.

The World's Most Baffling "Unicycle" Puzzle

Young Austin Tightcollar was a dutiful son who visited his mother for dinner every Sunday. Austin lived in Rivergrove and his mom lived in Center City. Austin left promptly at noon after coffee hour at his church. Long ago he figured out that if he rode his unicycle at 15 miles an hour, he would get to her house an hour before dinner. But if he rode at the rate of 10 miles an hour, he would arrive an hour late for dinner.

Can you figure out at what speed Austin rode to arrive precisely at dinner time? Also, what was the distance between his home and his mother's?

The World's Most Baffling "Sentence" Puzzle

"Attention, all puzzlers! Attention, all puzzlers! Rally round and listen carefully. What do the following three sentences have in common?

Madam, I'm Adam.
Able was I ere I saw Elba.
Egad, a base tone denotes a bad age."

The World's Most Baffling "Groucho" Puzzle

> *"Any puzzle club that would accept me as a member is a club I wouldn't want to join!"*

PUZZLE CLUB ENTRANCE PROBLEM					
4	5	6	7	8	9
61	52	63	94	46	?

It looks like Groucho is in no mood to join our club. I wonder if he could have solved the above entrance problem? All you have to do is to figure out what the last number should be!

The World's Most Baffling "Diet" Puzzle

Our overweight diner is so flabbergasted over the size of the bill that he has lapsed into number talk at the end of his reply to the waiter. Can you translate his numbers into words?

The World's Most Baffling "Theatre" Puzzle

The local Chamber Music Society, lately known as the Catgut Four, presented their fall concert last night, and it was a sellout here in Corncrib, Iowa. The entire town of 120 people showed up and paid a total of $120 for the evening's entertainment. Tickets were priced as follows: men paid $5, women paid $2, and children paid 10 cents each. Can you figure out how many men, women, and children were at the concert?

The World's Most Baffling "Betting" Puzzle

J. Wellington Moneybags is back in town with a new bag of bets to separate the local wagering gentry from their money. We were sitting around the Bits-and-Grits Coffee Shop one night when Wellington presented us with this one. Putting a sheet of paper and a pencil on the table, he said, "I'll wager anyone a hundred dollars that I can prove that you can take four away from four and be left with eight."

We all knew that there had to be a trick to it, but finally Elmer Wormwood put a dollar on the table and said: "Take it or leave it, Moneybags. My money says, 'You can't prove it.'"

Well, of course, J. Wellington took it and showed everyone that you can indeed take four away from four and end up with eight. How did he do it?

The World's Most Baffling "Floating" Puzzle

"See how easy it is! Now I'll show you how to make a solid piece of steel float on water."

"I say, Lorenzo, do you have to?"

Uncle Lorenzo is quite an after-dinner entertainer. Although not in the same class as J. Wellington, he pulls off a good one now and then. He's not kidding about being able to make a solid piece of steel float on water. See if you can figure out how it's done before turning to the answer section.

The World's Most Baffling "Arrow" Puzzle

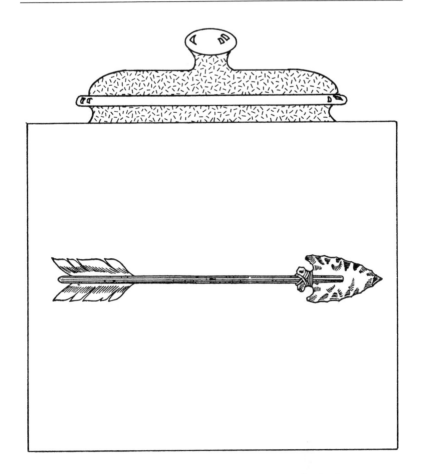

Here's a clever bit of trickery that will fool them every time. On a small piece of cardboard, draw an arrow, the fancier the better. Next, prop the drawing up against some object on the table so that the arrow points to the right. Now, bet anyone that you can make the arrow turn around and point to the left without touching the card or moving the table in anyway. It sounds impossible, but . . .

The World's Most Baffling "Monkey" Puzzle

Tony's organ is sadly out of tune, but his staying powers are inexhaustible, and nothing short of a contribution from each person in the picture will bribe him to stop grinding and move on to other quarters.

Now that his audience is ready to capitulate, can you show Jocko the shortest possible route by which he can move from window to window with his little tin cup to collect his dues? The monkey must start from his present position and end his tour by resting on his master's shoulders.

The World's Most Baffling "Jumping" Puzzle

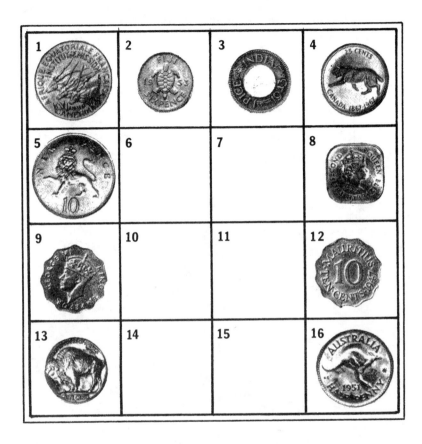

This is an interesting problem that should keep you occupied for some time. Lay out a four-by-four square playing board like the one shown above. Next, place ten coins on the indicated squares. Now for the fun. You must remove nine coins from the board by jumping one over another as in checkers. Here, however, you are only allowed to jump either horizontally or vertically. To begin, you are allowed to slide one of the coins to *any* empty square. From that point on you must use only jumping moves.

The World's Most Baffling "Dirt" Puzzle

"*Another urgent message from Panama. Jackson is always having trouble with his excavation calculations. See if you can figure this one out, Henderson. How many cubic yards of dirt are there in a ditch that is 12 yards wide, 20 feet deep, and 600 feet long?*"

"*I'll need pencil and paper to work that one out!*"

President Theodore Roosevelt is dealing with a problem concerning his famous canal. Can you help Mr. Henderson answer the president's question?

The World's Most Baffling "Triangle" Puzzle

Down along the Nile people often contemplated pyramids and triangles. The young woman shown here is trying to calculate the number of triangles depicted in the above drawing. There are many different-size triangles within the drawing. Let's see how many you can find in 60 seconds.

The World's Most Baffling "Devilish" Puzzle

Although the Devil has nothing to do with this little puzzle, you may find it diabolically hard to solve. The mustachioed gentleman here wants to bet that you cannot arrange three sixes so that they represent the number twenty. I have no idea as to the nature of his bet, but I would advise you to solve it just for fun.

The World's Most Baffling "Brush-off" Puzzle

Here's a puzzle that's over a hundred years old. Place a coin on your outstretched hand, and challenge people to try to brush it off using only a soft-bristle clothes brush. No striking or knocking of your hand is allowed. They'll find that no matter how hard they try, the bristles just cannot get under the coin to move it. This is one time when you will definitely not get the brush-off.

The World's Most Baffling "Advice" Puzzle

B
_____

Faults man quarrels wife faults

The battling Brewsters are at it again. Sixty years of marriage have not mellowed this twosome. Their friends would be well-advised to heed the advice proffered in the rebus puzzle printed at the top of this page.

The World's Most Baffling "Entrance" Puzzle

This young lady is on her way to a costume party for charity being presented at the local zoo. However, there is no one in attendance to let her in. On the fence post there's a badly lettered sign with instructions on how to proceed. Can you interpret this sign so that Cleo will be on time for the ball?

The World's Most Baffling "Trig" Puzzle

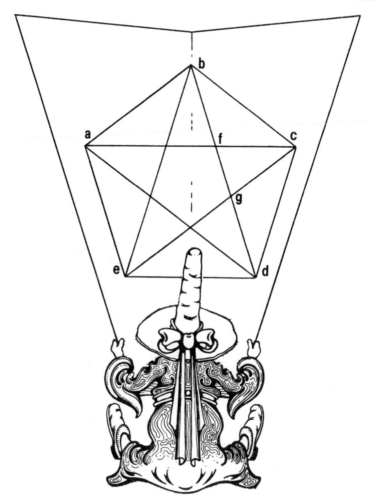

Sweet Eloise is pictured here pondering an interesting poser in trigonometry. She's trying to count all of the triangles, large and small, in the above drawing. Some examples are abf, fcg, abc, etc. In this type of problem, the puzzler is given only one chance to come up with the correct number.

ANSWERS

Answers

And now for the answers! We've done our best to make the solutions as clear as possible. Occasionally, a puzzle will have more the one solution. When this happens, we try to give the reader the answer that is most often associated with the problem. Sometimes a puzzle will have so many solutions that it is not practical to give more than one. Thankfully, most problems in this book have only one solution.

"Number" Puzzle (page 6).

$$55 \frac{5}{5}$$

"Juggling" Puzzle (page 7). You certainly have to give the "thumbs up" to this solution. In fact, you have to be "all thumbs" to make it work. The illustration tells all. As Mr. Fields said, "One minute's practice and you're a juggler!"

"Business Card" Puzzle (page 8). Place the card near the edge of the table. Make sure that the card is tilted away from you. Now stand in front of the card with your arms apart, table high. Cup your hands and swing your arms vigorously inward, clapping your hands together a few inches in front of the card. The sharp puff of wind from your hands will flip the card over. A little practice will reward you with a first-class puzzle.

Desmond's brother, Handsome Harry Hustlemore, is shown here demonstrating the correct way to execute this puzzle.

"Ornament" Puzzle (page 9). Before cutting the string, take a loop of cord in the middle and knot it firmly together. Now take a pair of scissors and snip through the loop. As you promised, you have cut the string in two without causing any harm to the ornament. I'll take the red Mercedes, please!

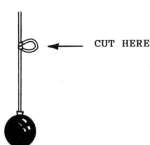

CUT HERE

"Card" Puzzle (page 10). The explanation is simplicity itself. Just be sure that the total of the first card plus the third card adds up to the value of the middle card. Simple . . . but very, very good!

"Bottle Cap" Puzzle (page 11). This drawing illustrates one of many solutions to this type of problem.

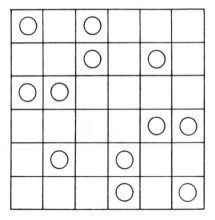

"Cross" Puzzle (page 12). Here's the solution Sexton Winslow was looking for.

"Business Survey" Puzzle (page 13). Let's break down the results of Sylvester's mustard survey.

(1) Of the 234 people who use hot mustard, 90 of them only use hot mustard (234 − 144 = 90).
(2) Of the 213 people who use mild mustard, 69 of them only use mild mustard (213 − 144 = 69).

This means that we had 3 groups of people:

(1) Those who used only hot mustard $= 90$
(2) Those who used only mild mustard $= 69$
(3) Those who used both hot and mild
mustard $= \underline{144}$
$\qquad\qquad\qquad$ Total $= 303$ people

Sylvester's figures indicate that 303 people had been surveyed, but their report stated that only 300 had been interviewed. Obviously, their report is flawed, something that the Volcano Mustard Company couldn't tolerate.

"Water and Wine" Puzzle (page 14). The answer is that there is as much water in the wine glass as there is wine in the water glass. The proof goes like this:

(1) Let's say that each glass contains 100 units of liquid and that the spoon holds 10 units of liquid.
(2) With the spoon Percy transfers 10 units of water from the water glass to the wine glass and stirs them both together.
(3) The wine glass now contains 110 units of liquid. When Percy now takes a spoonful of liquid from this glass he will be removing $\frac{1}{11}$ of each liquid. Thus he will have $9\frac{1}{11}$ units of wine and $\frac{10}{11}$ units of water in his spoon. This he pours into the water glass.
(4) The water glass now contains $90\frac{10}{11}$ units of water and $9\frac{1}{11}$ units of wine which totals up to 100 units of liquid.
(5) The wine glass contains $90\frac{10}{11}$ units of wine and $9\frac{1}{11}$ units of water, also 100 units of liquid.

A fair exchange!

"Elevator" Puzzle (page 15). The reason for his eccentric behavior is that this business giant happened to be a midget. Going down he had no trouble reaching the button for the first floor, but going up, he could only reach the button for the 40th floor. Since the buttons were all heat sensitive, he couldn't poke them with a pen or pencil. When he was able to ride all the way up to the 45th floor that was because another passenger got on the elevator and could press the right button for him.

"Cardboard" Puzzle (page 16). Cut the cross along the two center lines indicated below, and rearrange the four pieces into the shape of a square as shown. You'll note that the square is as high and as wide as the original cross.

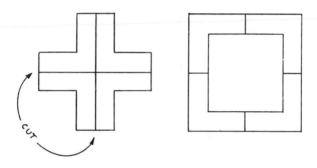

"Planchette" Puzzle (page 17).

"India Squares" Puzzle (page 18). The puzzle measures 8 feet to a side. You'll find the following number of squares:

8 × 8 feet	1
6 × 6 feet	4
4 × 4 feet	9
2 × 2 feet	18
1 × 1 foot	8
Total	40 squares

"Diner" Puzzle (page 19). Here's a translation of Harriet's diner lingo:

ADAM	8384
AND	803
EVE	626
ON	50
A	8
RAFT	9871

"Geography" Puzzle (page 20). The letter in question is the second *C* in the second line reading across. The four city names radiating from this letter are: Chattanooga, Chicago, Columbus, and Council Bluffs.

"Cocoa Tin" Puzzle (page 21). The secret to this problem is sweet indeed. Place the box on a square-topped table with one edge of the tin along one edge of the table. Position the tin one box width away from one corner of the table (the width *a* equals the width *b*). Now, take the ruler and place one end of it on the corner of the table and measure to the left top back corner of the box. This will be equal to the box's major diagonal line.

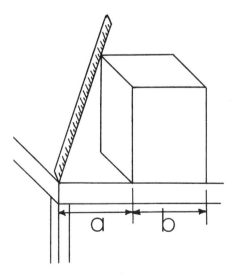

"Racing" Puzzle (page 22). First place was number 6, second place was number 7, and third place was number 9.

"Counter" Puzzle (page 23). The moves are: 2 to 6, 1 to 5, 8 to 2, 7 to 1, 4 to 8, 3 to 7, 10 to 4, 9 to 3, 6 to 10, 5 to 9.

"Lighthouse" Puzzle (page 24). Leroy reached down and pulled the plug out of the bottom of the tub which allowed the water to run out faster than it was coming in. Another puzzler saved!

"Bathtub" Puzzle (page 25). It will take exactly 5 minutes to fill Ma Bascomb's tub. To solve this problem we must first break down the times into seconds.

(1) The cold water tap takes 400 seconds to fill the tub, which comes to $\frac{1}{400}$ of the tub in 1 second.
(2) The hot water takes 480 seconds, which comes to $\frac{1}{480}$ of the tub in 1 second.
(3) The water drains out of the tub in 800 seconds, which comes to $\frac{1}{800}$ of the tub in 1 second.

If we use 4800 as a common denominator we come up with the equation:

$$\frac{12}{4800} + \frac{10}{4800} - \frac{6}{4800} = \frac{16}{4800} = \frac{1}{300}$$

This is equal to the net amount of water added to the tub every second. Thus, it will take 300 seconds, or 5 minutes, to fill the tub.

"Antique" Puzzle (page 26). Here are two solutions to the problem.

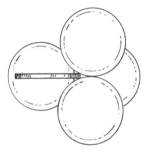

"Touching " Puzzle (page 27). First arrange two coins touching on the table. Then place two more coins on top so that all four are touching. Lastly, place the fifth coin upright as shown and you will have five coins all touching. All coins of course must be of the same size or denomination.

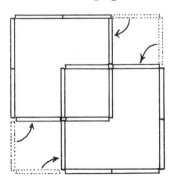

"Telephone Pole" Puzzle (page 28).

"Milling" Puzzle (page 29). Angus will have to bring exactly 111⅑ pounds of corn to the mill if he wants to walk away with 100 pounds of cornmeal. (111.111 pounds minus 10% equals 100 pounds.)

"Golf Tees" Puzzle (page 30).

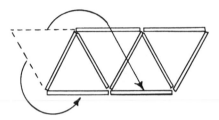

"Soda Straws" Puzzle (page 31). Add the five straws to the ones on the table so that they spell out the number nine. How else?

NINE

"Math" Puzzle (page 32).

$$123 - 45 - 67 + 89 = 100$$

"Magic Square" Puzzle (page 33). The answer to the Magic Square is 2, 3, 1 in the first row; 1, 2, 3 in the middle row; and 3, 1, 2 in the last row. Or, 3, 1, 2 in the first row; 1, 2, 3 in the middle row; and 2, 3, 1 in the last row.

"Line" Puzzle (page 34).

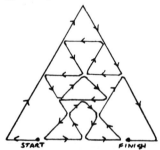

"Sculpture" Puzzle (page 35).

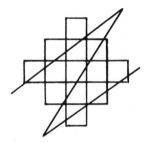

"Ice Cream Stick" Puzzle (page 36). The answer is simple. Just turn the page upside down, and the equation will read correctly.

"Ports of Call" Puzzle (page 37). (1) Los Angeles (2) London (3) Rio de Janeiro (4) Lisbon (5) Charleston (6) Marseilles (7) Montego Bay (8) Montevideo (9) Brest (10) Leningrad

"Shooting" Puzzle (page 38). The 3 birds are 25, 6, and 19.

"Thimble" Puzzle (page 39).

"Zoo" Puzzle (page 40).

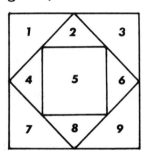

"Mind-Over-Matter" Puzzle (page 41). The first thing to keep in mind is that you should use a small, very thin glass to cover the coin and match. Inside the glass, the paper end of the match should be as close as possible to the side of the glass. The reason for these considerations is that you will be using static electricity to move the match. Remove a comb from your pocket and briskly comb your hair a few times. This will generate a magnetic charge in your comb. Next, bring the comb's edge up to the side of the glass as near as possible to the end of the match inside. Move the comb back and forth. There should be enough attraction between the comb and the match to cause the match to move or even fall off the coin. (If you are bald, like your author, then you must recruit an assistant from the audience. Those are the breaks.)

"Clock" Puzzle (page 42). Although several answers to this puzzle are possible, this one is usually considered the principal solution to this very old but good problem.

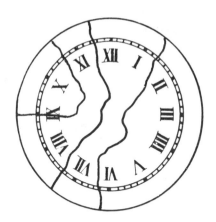

"Poem" Puzzle (page 43). Ms. Gotrock's ditty goes like this:

> Too wise you are;
>   too wise you be.
> I see you are
>   too wise for me.

"Baseball" Puzzle (page 44). Starting with the "I" on the bottom side of the frame, read around the frame clockwise. The quotation is Yogi Berra's famous observation, "It gets late out there early."

"Word" Puzzle (page 45). The five letter word is *dozen*. The equation should read:

$$99 + 9 = 9 \text{ dozen}$$

"Big Fish" Puzzle (page 46). We calculate that the head was 60 feet long, the tail 180 feet, and the body 240 feet, which gives an overall length of 480 feet. Now, that's some fish story!

"State" Puzzle (page 47). The great state of *ALABAMA,* of course!

"Dice" Puzzle (page 48). Before you pick up the dice, secretly moisten your right forefinger. Rub this finger across the face of one of the dice. Now, place the second die against this moistened face, and press the two dice together with your thumb and forefinger. Still holding the two dice like that, place them across the die on the table and let go. The two dice will stick together and stay balanced on top of the third die. Once again, you've made your point!

"Checker" Puzzle (page 49). White to move and win: 24 to 19; 16 to 23; 31 to 26; 23 to 30; 17 to 21.

"Shopping" Puzzle (page 50). She used a fifty, two twenties, a five and four twos.

"Proofreading" Puzzle (page 51). The first error is using the word *their* instead of *there*. The second error is spelling *error* as *errer*. The third error is saying, in the paragraph, that there are *three* errors, when in truth there are only *two* errors in the paragraph.

"Handshake" Puzzle (page 52). There will be 28 handshakes in all. Santa *A* shakes hands with seven other santas. Santa *B*, having already shaken hands with Santa *A*, has only six other santas to shake hands with. Santa *C* has only five to shake hands with, etc. The total number of shakes is:

$$7+6+5+4+3+2+1 = 28$$

"Maze" Puzzle (page 53). The secret to the Hampton Court Maze is simple: always keep your right hand touching the bushes on the right-hand side of the path as you walk through the maze.

"Logic" Puzzle (page 54). Every *INTERIOR* number in the triangle is found by multiplying together the two closest numbers to it in the line of numbers above it. Example: 8 is the product of 2 × 4, 32 is the product of 2 × 16, etc.

```
                    2
                 2 — 2
              2 — 4 — 2
           2 — 8 — 8 — 2
        2 — 16 — 64 — 16 — 2
     2   32  1024  1024  32   2
```

"Sticky Taffy" Puzzle (page 55). In the answer below, the equation reads five minus four equals the square root of one, or one equals one.

"Nail" Puzzle (page 56).

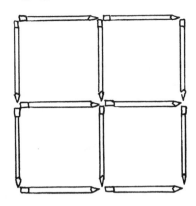

"Crown" Puzzle (page 57).

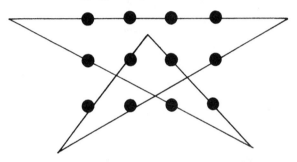

"Waiter" Puzzle (page 58). Put your face down close to the penny and blow on it. A good hefty gust of wind should get it off the plate. Choose a plate with a small sloping rim.

"Mental" Puzzle (page 59). The answer is simple. The first middle digit of any difference between two three-digit numbers (when the first three-digit number is reversed and the smaller is subtracted from the larger) will always be nine. Also, the first and third digits will always add up to nine. So, if the last digit is eight, the first digit must be a one, and the second digit is of course nine. Works every time.

"Presidential" Puzzle (page 60). The fourth requirement is that he must get elected.

"Rebus" Puzzles (page 61).

(1) "Of course, sir, *you understand you are under oath.*"
(2) "We're in for *a bad spell of weather.*"
(3) "My name is *Mary Overton.*"

"H₂O" Puzzle (page 62).

"H$_2$O" Puzzle (page 62). (a–bc) indicates *a* moving from position *a* to a position touching two other coins *b* and *c*. The moves are: (1–56), (3–14), (4–58), (5–23), (2–54).

"Rearranging" Puzzle (page 63).

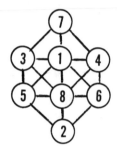

"Addition" Puzzle (page 64).

$$
\begin{array}{r}
8 \\
8 \\
8 \\
88 \\
\underline{888} \\
1,000
\end{array}
$$

"Real Estate" Puzzle (page 65).

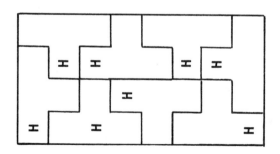

"Campaign Button" Puzzle (page 66).

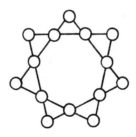

"Weighing" Puzzle (page 67). The weighings go as follows: (1) Put the 5-pound weight in one pan and the 9-pound weight in the other pan. Now, weigh out 4 pounds of tea in the 5-pound pan. (2) Remove the weights and place the 4 pounds of tea in one pan and weigh out another 4 pounds of tea. (3) Weigh another 4 pounds. (4) Weigh another 4 pounds. The remainder is also 4 pounds. For weighings (5), (6), (7), (8), and (9), divide each 4-pound portion into two 2-pound portions using the scales. Another mystery of the East solved!

"Mystical Square" Puzzle (page 68).

20	1	12
3	11	19
10	21	2

"Substitution" Puzzle (page 69).

$$\begin{array}{r} 850 \\ 850 \\ \underline{29786} \\ 31486 \end{array}$$

"Progression" Puzzle (page 70). The numbers are written in alphabetical order. *E*ight, *f*ive, *f*our, *n*ine, etc.

"Pencil" Puzzle (page 71).

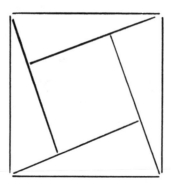

"Train" Puzzle (page 72). Engine *T* pushes car *B* up into *C*. *T* then goes around and pushes car *A* up and couples it onto *B*. *T* then goes around to the right side and pulls *B* and *A* down into the right siding. *T* then goes around and up the left siding into *C* and pushes *A* onto the main track. *T* leaves *B* on the right siding, goes to get *A*, and pushes *A* up into the left siding. *T* then returns to its starting position on the main track.

"Stirring" Puzzle (page 73).

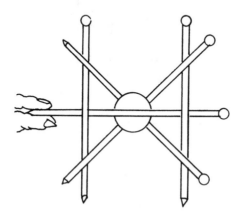

"Map" Puzzle (page 74). The cities and towns are all in California.

"O. Henry" Puzzle (page 75). To start with, $1.87 minus 60 pennies comes to $1.27. Della would still need at least *two* more pennies to make this amount. That means that she would have had *62* pennies, not *60* as stated. Who was his editor anyway? He should get coal in his stocking, at the very least.

"Time" Puzzle (page 76). First off, the broken clock will show the correct time twice a day, for a total of fourteen times a week. On the other hand, the clock that loses an hour a day will be correct only once every twelve days. So, for accuracy, a stopped clock beats a slow one every time.

"Pie" Puzzle (page 77). The pie can be cut into eleven different-size pieces.

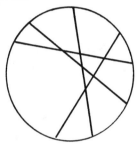

"Domino" Puzzle (page 78). The answer is that you cannot cover the checkerboard. Remember, one domino, while covering two squares, will always cover one red square and one black square. However, when we cut the two opposite end squares from the board we removed two squares of the *same* color. In our example, the board was left with 32 black squares and 30 red squares. After you place 30 dominoes on the board, you will be left with two red squares that will *not* be touching, thus making it impossible to cover them with the last domino. On any checkerboard, no two squares of the same color will ever be side by side.

"Alphabet" Puzzle (page 79). You would place the letter Z below the line with the other letters it rhymes with (the *e* sounding letters).

"Chocolate Candy" Puzzle (page 80). Let's work backwards from the eight pieces of candy. Since this was two-thirds of what the third traveller found when he woke up, he must have found twelve chocolates on the plate. In turn, twelve candies must have been two-thirds of what the second traveller found when he woke up. So, he saw eighteen candies on the plate. Finally, eighteen candies had to be two-thirds of what the first traveller found when he woke up. That means that the dish originally contained twenty-seven chocolates.

"Tire" Puzzle (page 81). She recommended that he take one lug nut off the other three tires and use them to mount the fourth tire. It worked, and we drove slowly into the next town. There we fixed our bad tire, and bought five new lug nuts.

"Fencing" Puzzle (page 82). There may be other answers to this problem, but this is the only one that this author is aware of.

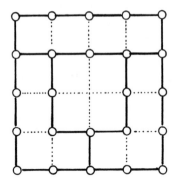

"Shape" Puzzle (page 83). The object is a short wooden cylinder with a notch cut into it.

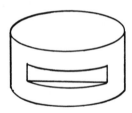

"Family" Puzzle (page 84). There are four daughters and three sons.

"Match" Puzzle (page 85). Take away two matches forming each of the lower corners and the center match from the top row. This will leave you with three squares.

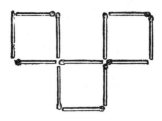

"Unicycle" Puzzle (page 86). The distance between Austin's home and that of his mother is 60 miles. Now, if he rode 15 miles an hour for four hours he would have arrived at 4 PM, an hour too early for dinner. On the other hand, if he rode 10 miles an hour for six hours, he would have arrived at 6 PM, a full hour too late. So, Austin figured out that a steady 12 miles an hour for five hours would bring him to the table at exactly 5 PM, just as mom was putting the melon in front of his place at the table.

"Sentence" Puzzle (page 87). The one thing that the three sentences have in common is that . . . they all read the same both forward and backwards. They're all palindromes.

"Groucho" Puzzle (page 88). Well, the last number should be 18. Every number in the bottom row is the square of the number above it turned around. As an example, the first number in the top row is 4. The square of 4 is 16. Turn 16 around and you get 61, the first number in the bottom row. In the last row we have 9 squared, which gives us 81, when turned around we have 18, the answer.

"Diet" Puzzle (page 89). The number 102004180 translates: "I ought to owe nothing for I ate nothing."

"Theatre" Puzzle (page 90). The totals were: 17 men paid $85; 13 women paid $26; and 90 children paid $9, for a total of $120.

"Betting" Puzzle (page 91). This answer only proves that it's how you look at a problem that counts. J. Wellington ignored the pencil and picked up the sheet of paper. He then proceeded to tear off the four corners of the paper. When he was done the sheet had eight corners, clearly proving that you can take away four corners from four corners and be left with eight.

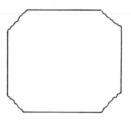

"Floating" Puzzle (page 92). First, fill a wide-mouth glass to the top with water. Next, cut out a square of tissue paper that is a little wider than a sewing needle. Then get a steel sewing needle and place it in the middle of the paper. Gently place the tissue with the needle on it in the center of the glass of water. After a minute or two the paper will soak up enough water to sink to the bottom of the glass, leaving the needle floating in the middle supported by the surface tension of the water. You'll then have a solid piece of steel floating in a glass of water.

"Arrow" Puzzle (page 93). All you need to perform this feat is a tall, straight-sided glass filled with water. Place the glass in front of the arrow on the card and see what happens. The water, acting like a lens, will cause the arrow to be optically reversed. When you look at the arrow through the glass, it will appear to be pointing left.

"Monkey" Puzzle (page 94). Jocko took the windows in the following order: 10, 11, 12, 8, 4, 3, 7, 6, 2, 1, 5, 9. This route travels the wide space between the bottom and middle rows of windows only twice. This puzzle is from Sam Loyd, America's greatest puzzle creator.

"Jumping" Puzzle (page 95). Start off by moving the coin in square number 8 to empty number 10. The following nine jumping moves will remove nine of the ten coins from the board: 9 to 11, 1 to 9, 13 to 5, 16 to 8, 4 to 12, 12 to 10, 3 to 1, 1 to 9, and 9 to 11.

"Dirt" Puzzle (page 96). I'm afraid that President Roosevelt is having a little fun at Henderson's expense. There isn't any dirt in a ditch. It's empty.

"Triangle" Puzzle (page 97). There are four sizes of triangles in the drawing. The smallest size has 7 triangles. The next size has 3, the third largest has 3, and the largest has 1. This comes to a total of 14 triangles in all.

"Devilish" Puzzle (page 98). Set up the equation as follows:

$$\frac{6 + 6}{.6} = 20$$

Twelve divided by six-tenths will give you a result of twenty.

"Advice" Puzzle (page 100). "Be above quarrels between man and wife. There are faults on both sides." The *B* is above the word *quarrels*, which in turn is between the words *man* and *wife*. Finally, the word *faults* appears on the sides of the words *man* and *wife*.

"Entrance" Puzzle (page 101). The sign says: "TO OPEN GATE PUSH!"

"Trig" Puzzle (page 102). There are 35 different triangles in Eloise's picture. The breakdown is as follows:

Type abf = 10
Type ace = 5
Type bfc = 5
Type cfg = 5
Type abc = 5
Type bge = 5

"Cat and Dog" Puzzle (page 128) Chasing cats and solving puzzles is tiring work, so Jackie could only come up with one answer to this puzzle. I'm sure, however, that there must be additional solutions to her problem. Jackie's answer is:

$$\begin{array}{r} 430 \\ + 926 \\ \hline 1356 \end{array}$$

Index to Puzzles and Answers

Answer pages are in italics.

About the Author

Charles Barry Townsend has been writing books and editing magazines on puzzles, games, and magic for over 16 years. He is the author of ten books, including *The World's Best Puzzles*, *The World's Most Challenging Puzzles*, and *The World's Toughest Puzzles*, and for three years his monthly column, "Puzzles and Problems," graced the pages of *Creative Computing* and *Sync* magazines. He currently lives on Hilton Head Island, South Carolina, where he is working on his fifth book for Sterling, *The World's Hardest Puzzles*.

The author's dog, Jackie, challenges the reader to solve her "Cat and Dog" Puzzle. You have to create a correct mathematical expression by substituting a different number for each letter in the puzzle. However, the same number must be used for each occurrence of the same letter. As an example, if you substituted 9 for *G* in *DOG*, then you would also have to substitute 9 for the *G* in *BANG*.